Usborne English

Level 1

The Emperor and the Nightingale

Retold by Mairi Mackinnon

Illustrated by Lorena Alvarez

English language consultant: Peter Viney

Contents

3

The Emperor and the Nightingale

24

About Hans Christian Andersen

25

Activities

30

Word list

You can listen to the story online here:
www.usborneenglishreaders.com/
emperorandthenightingale

A long time ago, in China, there was a great city. Next to the city there were lovely gardens. They were full of tall trees and summer flowers. In the middle, there was a beautiful white palace.

In the palace lived the Emperor, the most important man in China.

The Emperor loved walking in his gardens every day. He loved reading about them, too. People came to the gardens from all over China, and wrote many long books about them.

One day, the Emperor was reading a new book about his gardens. "You can walk through the gardens for hours," it said. "Then you come to the forest, and after the forest is the sea. In the forest, in the evening, you sometimes hear the nightingale. Its song is the loveliest music in the world."

"Nightingale?" said the Emperor. "What is this nightingale? Why don't I know about it?"

He told his Prime Minister, "Bring me the nightingale, now!"

The Prime Minister didn't know anything about a nightingale. He asked all the servants, but they didn't know.

Then one little servant girl from the kitchens said, "Oh yes, I know the nightingale. Her nest is in the forest near my mother's house. I love listening to her. I can show you."

The Prime Minster and the other servants went with her to the forest. They heard a sound.

"Ah, beautiful!" they said.

"That's not the nightingale," said the girl. "Those are just cows."

Soon they heard another sound.
"Wonderful music!" they said.
"Those are frogs!"
the girl laughed.

Finally they heard it – a beautiful sad song in the trees. Everyone listened quietly. When the nightingale finished her song, the Prime Minister said, "That was lovely. Please come to the palace and sing for the Emperor tomorrow."

"Are you sure?" asked the nightingale. "Really, the best place to hear my song is out here in the forest."

"The Emperor is asking you," said the kitchen girl. "Please come."

The next day, the palace was full of bright lights and flowers. There were people everywhere. Everyone wanted to see the nightingale.

A little brown bird flew into the palace hall. "She's not very pretty," they said. Then the nightingale started to sing.

Everyone listened. Nobody moved. The little bird's song filled the hall. When she stopped singing, the Emperor had tears in his eyes.

"Wonderful," he said. "Little bird, please stay with me always."

They made a golden cage for the nightingale. Every morning and every evening, twelve servants tied ribbons to her legs and took her out of her cage.

The nightingale didn't like living in a cage. She didn't like flying with ribbons on her legs, but she didn't say anything.

The Emperor loved his nightingale, and so did everyone in the palace. All the princesses tried to sing nightingale songs. Clever people wrote books all about her.

"So many big, heavy books about a little bird," thought the nightingale. "It's very strange."

One day, a present arrived for the Emperor. It was from his friend, the Emperor of Japan.

Inside was a little bird made of gold and jewels, with a golden key. "Look," said the Emperor. "It's another nightingale!"

"Can it sing?" asked the Prime Minister. "Let's hear it singing with *our* nightingale."

The Emperor turned the key, and the golden bird played a tune. It turned around and around, and its jewels shone like stars.

The nightingale tried to sing with the little clockwork toy, but her song was too different. Quietly, she flew out of the room.

"Play the tune again!" said the Prime
Minister. The golden bird played and
played. "Wonderful!" said the Prime
Minister.

"Where is the real nightingale?"
asked the Emperor, but nobody knew.

"The clockwork nightingale is better,"
said the Prime Minister. "It's much
prettier, and it always sings the same
song. I like that."

So then of course everyone said the same thing. Only the little kitchen girl thought, "I'm sorry about the real nightingale. I hope she is happy in the forest."

Every morning and evening, the Emperor turned the golden key and the little toy bird played its tune. On special days, servants took the golden nightingale out into the city. Hundreds of people came to see and hear it.

Then, one terrible day, the Emperor turned the golden key and the golden bird turned around once… and stopped.

"Where is the Prime Minister?" asked the Emperor – but the Prime Minister couldn't do anything.

"Where is the palace doctor?" asked the Prime Minister – but the palace doctor couldn't help. "You need a clockmaker," he said.

Carefully, the old palace clockmaker opened the bird's little body.

He worked for hours. Finally he said, "That's better."

"The clockwork in your toy bird can easily break," he said. "You can play it once a year, but no more than that."

The Emperor was sad, but once a year was better than nothing. He thanked the clockmaker. After that, the golden nightingale played its tune every year on the Emperor's birthday.

Then a few years later, the Emperor was ill. All the doctors in the palace and the city tried to help him, but the Emperor was an old man and he wasn't strong.

He lay still in his bed, with tears in his eyes. He couldn't eat, and when he tried to sleep, he had nightmares. His room was full of ghosts.

"The Emperor is dying," the ghosts
said. "They are choosing a new emperor
now." They talked about the Emperor,
and all the good and bad things in his life.

"Stop!" the Emperor tried to say, but he
couldn't speak. He didn't want to listen to
the ghosts. He saw the golden nightingale
beside his bed, but he couldn't move and
turn its golden key. He closed his eyes.

Then a beautiful sound filled the room.
The Emperor opened his eyes again…
and there was the nightingale, the *real*
nightingale. She sang her lovely song, and
the ghosts were gone.

"My little friend," said the Emperor.
"You came back! I feel so much better."
The nightingale sang again, and the
Emperor fell asleep. He slept for a long
time without nightmares. When he woke
again, the nightingale was still there.

"I'm sorry, my friend," the Emperor said. "I was wrong about the golden nightingale. I never want to hear it again – but please, stay with me now."

"I can't live in a cage," said the nightingale, "but I can make my nest in the palace gardens, and visit you every day. I can fly through the city and the forest, and tell you all about them. You are going to be strong and well again, my Emperor."

"How can I thank you?"
asked the Emperor.

"You are my friend," said the little bird.
"You don't need to say any more. Listen,
your servants are coming. I must go."

Slowly and carefully, the servants
opened the door – but their Emperor was
not dead. He was sitting up and smiling
and saying, "Good morning!"

About Hans Christian Andersen

Hans Christian Andersen lived in Denmark over 100 years ago. His family was very poor. When he was a child, he didn't have many friends, but he loved stories.

In 1837, Andersen wrote a book of stories for children. It was very popular, and Andersen wrote many more stories between 1838-1872. Some other stories by Andersen are *The Emperor's New Clothes*, *The Little Mermaid* and *The Snow Queen*.

Andersen loved visiting other countries, but he never went to China. When he wrote *The Emperor and the Nightingale*, in 1843, people were very interested in China and the East. They loved the story of the rich Emperor and the ordinary little bird with the beautiful voice.

Activities

The answers are on page 32.

What happened when?

Can you put the pictures and sentences in order?

A.

They heard a beautiful sad song in the trees.

B.

"What is this nightingale?"

C.

"Please, stay with me now."

D.

The golden bird turned around once... and stopped.

E.

"The nightingale's nest is in the forest near my mother's house."

F.

"Look! It's another nightingale!"

Talk about things in the story

Choose the right word to finish each sentence.

secret   golden   sad   important

wonderful   real   happy   wooden

1.

In the palace lived the most
.... man in China.

2.

".............. music!" they said.

3.

They made a............. cage.

4.

"Where is the ....
nightingale?"

Are you sure?

One word in each sentence is wrong.
Can you choose the right word instead?

1.

"Those are just trees."
cows   birds   flowers

2.

"She's not very happy."
big   brown   pretty

3.

All the servants tried to
sing nightingale songs.

people   princesses   birds

4.

Then a few years later, the
Emperor was strange.

hungry   sorry   ill

What do they want?

Choose the right sentence for each person.

A. I hope the nightingale is happy.

B. I hope the nightingale is near.

A. I want to make it better.

B. I want to sell it later.

The kitchen girl

The clockmaker

A. I want to see the ghosts.

B. I don't want to hear the ghosts.

A. I want to help the Emperor.

B. I want a new golden cage.

The Emperor

The nightingale

The end of the story

Choose **three** sentences that are true.

1. The servants stayed outside the room.

2. The Emperor was dying.

3. The Emperor wanted to thank the nightingale.

4. The nightingale and the Emperor were friends again.

5. The nightingale stayed in the palace.

6. The Emperor was happy.

Word list

cage (n) a kind of box made of wood or metal. You keep an animal or a bird in a cage so that it can't run or fly away.

clockmaker (n) a clockmaker makes and repairs clocks.

clockwork (n) the machine parts inside a clock that make it work.

doctor (n) a doctor's job is to take care of sick people and help them to get better.

emperor (n) someone who is even more powerful and important than a king.

fill (v) to make something full, or to be in every part of something.

finally (adv) after a long time.

frog (n) a small animal, usually green, that lives around water or in wet places.

ghost (n) some people believe that when a person dies, they can become a ghost. In stories, ghosts are usually unhappy or frightening.

hall (n) the biggest and most important room in a palace. A hall can also be the first room in a house.

ill (adj) not well, sick. When you are ill, you often have to stay in bed. When you are very ill, you can die.

jewel (n) a precious stone. For example, a diamond is a jewel.

key (n) you use a key to lock a room (to close it so that no one else can go in), or to make a clock work.

nest (n) a bird makes a nest for its eggs. Many birds make nests in trees.

nightingale (n) a small brown bird that sings a beautiful song in the evening or at night.

nightmare (n) a horrible and frightening dream.

palace (n) the home of a king or emperor.

prime minister (n) a minister works for a king or government, and the Prime Minister is the most important person in a government.

ribbon (n) a long, thin piece of cloth. People often tie ribbons around presents.

servant (n) someone who works for another person, especially in their home.

sound (n) anything that you hear is a sound.

tear (n) when you cry, the water in your eyes is called tears. You can cry tears because something is sad, or sometimes because something is beautiful and special.

tune (n) a short piece of music.

wonderful (adj) really good and special.

Answers

What happened when?
B, E, A, F, D, C

Talk about things in the story
1. important
2. wonderful
3. golden
4. real

Are you sure?
1. ~~trees~~ cows
2. ~~happy~~ pretty
3. ~~servants~~ princesses
4. ~~strange~~ ill

What do they want?
The kitchen girl: A
The clockmaker: A
The Emperor: B
The nightingale: A

The end of the story
3. True
4. True
6. True

You can find information about
other Usborne English Readers here:
www.usborneenglishreaders.com

Designed by Laura Nelson Norris
Edited by Jane Chisholm
With thanks to Andy Prentice
Digital imaging: Nick Wakeford

Page 24: picture of Hans Christian Andersen © The Granger Collection/Topfoto

First published in 2018 by Usborne Publishing Ltd.,
Usborne House, 83-85 Saffron Hill, London EC1N 8RT, England.
www.usborne.com Copyright © 2018 Usborne Publishing Ltd.